A MAD. CARNIVAL

Edited by
Al Feldstein

WARNER BOOKS

A Warner Communications Company

ARTIST: MORT DRUCKER   WRITER: LARRY SIEGEL

THE
ECCHORCIST

BETWEEN THE DEVIL AND THE HOLY SEE DEPT.

Remember the good old days when Hollywood used to make horror movies about vampires, werewolves, zombies, seventy foot apes and other assorted monsters? Let's face it, they were all disgusting creatures, but there was still something kinda harmless and loveable about them. Well, those days are gone forever. Today's film makers have come up with something *really* disgusting. Yessiree, you screamed at "Frankenstein," you shrieked at "King Kong," you shuddered at "Dracula" and you screamed at "King Kong," but take it from us . . . those guys were all a bunch of pussycats when compared to . . .

CCCCCCH!

Doctor, I'm glad you could come! I want you to look at my daughter!

You stupid &★⊚/△♢! Your Sister is a ☆♡!(#★*! Your Father is a†⊙♩/★★#! And your Mother kisses sweaty gym shirts!

There, there! Just relax! Everything will be all right!

Don't be silly, darling! you KNOW your Daddy is in Europe!

Oh, Mommy! I'm so frightened! I feel like something terrible is after me! Some ugly cursing snarling hideous monster that wants to take me away from you!

FlOOOOEY!

Tell me, have you noticed anything UNUSUAL about her behavior lately?

@#$% &©*¢!

Well, Doctor? what do you think . . . ?

Hmm! It's the strangest case of bronchitis I have ever seen!

Bronchitis?!? Why would anyone with bronchitis act like that?

That's what makes it so strange! I'll X-ray her brain to see if I can find out anything!

Very well! And while you're at it, would you try to find out something else . . . ?

What's that?

Where in the ☆©$¿*★ did she get such a ©¢!#★*© filthy mouth!

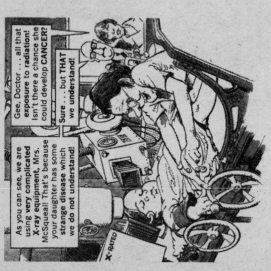

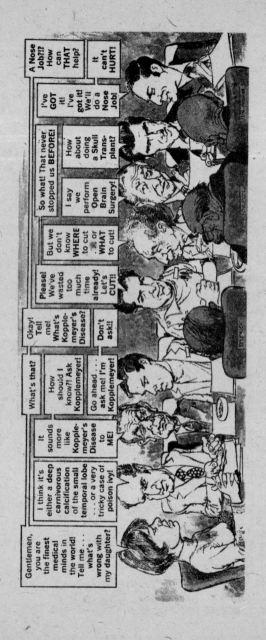

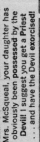

Hear that vicious, foul language? See the smoke pouring out of her mouth? Have you ever seen anything like that before, Father?

You've met ANOTHER child possessed by the Devil . . .?!?

Only ONCE!

No, I was visiting a Public School, and I accidentally walked into the Girls' Bathroom!

C'MERE, FATHER! I WANNA TELL YOU SOMETHING!

Look, Ravin! I'm only here as a favor to your Mother! I happen to know there's nothing wrong with you, so . . .

You want to tell me something?

YEAH, YOU %&#@!

I know you're not possessed by the Devil! So don't try your phony profanity! I've heard every foul word ever uttered! There's nothing horrible or nauseating you can say that will upset me!

Except that!!

Yahhh!

The Devil!

The Devil!

RING AROUND THE COLLAR! RING AROUND THE COLLAR!

I've been told the subject is only an 11-year old child, so this Exorcism shouldn't take too long! Where is she?

Hmm! On second thought, I'd better unpack! Now . . . these are the standard tools for an Exorcism: The vial of Holy Water to douse the evil spirit, the Crucifix to hold the Demon at bay, and the Hostess Cupcake . . .

You know it, Father! Exorcisms take time! Believe me, long about Midnight, you can get mighty hungry!

UPSTAIRS, ◇&◆*!◇, MAKING OUT WITH A TENNIS SHOE!

The Hostess CUPCAKE?!?

Well, Satan! Are you prepared to feel the Wrath of God?

GET LOST, CRUD! YOUR CHURCH STINKS! YOUR BISHOPS TAKE PAYOLA! AND THE POPE READS PLAYBOY!

Hmmmm! We always uncover something new about the enemy at these rituals!

You just learned something new about the Devil, Father Merry? What is it?

Well, for one thing, I think he's Protestant!

TWENTY-SEVEN HORRIBLE, DISGUSTING, NAUSEATING MINUTES LATER...

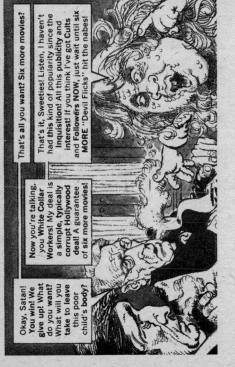

Okay, Satan! You win! We give up! What do you want? What will you take to leave this poor child's body?

That's all you want? Six more movies?

Now you're talking, you White Collar Workers! My deal is a simple, typically corrupt Hollywood deal! A guarantee of six more movies!

That's it, Sweeties! Listen, I haven't had this kind of popularity since the Inquisition! All this publicity and interest! If you think I've got Cults and Followers NOW, just wait until six MORE "Devil Flicks" hit the nabes!

Well, he's gone! And Ravin is FREE! But, how could you make that deal? How could you promise him six more movies?

That was easy! Have you seen the lines of people, waiting to see this movie? Have you seen the grosses it's piling up? What ELSE does Hollywood need to start a trend! SIX more "Devil Flicks"? Why, I'd guarantee SIXTY...SEVENTY!

Oh, well...that's "SHOW BIZ"!!

ONE DAY IN A RUN-DOWN

THE LIGHTER SIDE OF...

STAYiNG

YOUNG

ARTIST & WRITER: DAVE BERG

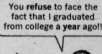

Hi! Like, how's my Old Lady?

Hear that? Kids today have a language all their own! When he says, "Old Lady," he means a young girl with whom he's having a meaningful relationship!

My wife has a real hang-up about getting old! I wish I could think of some way to make her feel young again!

Of course!! Why not ?! I'll start talking to her in the language of TODAY'S YOUTH!!

HI! HOW'S MY OLD LADY?

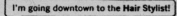

I'm going downtown to the **Hair Stylist!**

AGAIN?! I swear, men are worse than **women** with this youth kick! And today, they don't even call them **Barber Shops!** They're **Hair Stylists** so they can charge suckers like you a **small fortune!**

I like being fussed over!

A lot of **good** it'll do! You're **STILL** a forty-nine-year-old has-been!

Oh, **yeah?!?** I'll have you know that since I **started** going to these places, beautiful young women want to **hold my hand!**

HA! Like **WHO . . . ?**

Like the **Manicurists!!**

Why don't you face it! You're gray-haired, paunchy and middle-aged! As a stud, you're over the hill!

Oh, **yeah?!** Let me tell you something! I **still** get **second** looks from plenty of **young chicks!**

And I'll prove it to you **RIGHT NOW!** See that **cute little doll** coming this way? Well, **watch what happens!** Every time she **sees** me, she **kisses** me!

Hi, there . . .

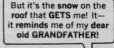

See that? What'd I **tell** you? There may be **snow** on the **roof,** but there's plenty of heat in the **furnace!**

But it's the **snow** on the **roof** that **GETS** me! It— it **reminds** me of my **dear** old **GRANDFATHER!**

Hey!! NOW, I recognize you! Weren't you **clean-shaven**—and didn't you wear a crew cut a couple of years ago?

That's right!

So why did you raise a full **beard** . . . and let your hair grow down to your **shoulders**?

I wanted to look **YOUNGER!!**

Really, Mom!! Ever since you turned **forty**, you've been on a **"Youth Jag"**!

Plastic surgery, health spas, dieting, hair color and all kinds of **crackpot rejuvenation medications!** Don't you think you're being a little **ridiculous?**

Not at all! People are **living longer** today! Which means I'm going to be **OLD** for a **LONG TIME!** It's going to affect my **business** and **social** life! So I figured, if I **HAVE** to be old . . .

David Berg

. . . I might as well be old as a **young-looking person!!**

ONE
AFTERNOON

AT A BUS STOP

FRIGHT INSTRUCTORS DEPT.

In the event they are hit by a passing car or incapacitated by a passing mugger, many people carry special cards, like the

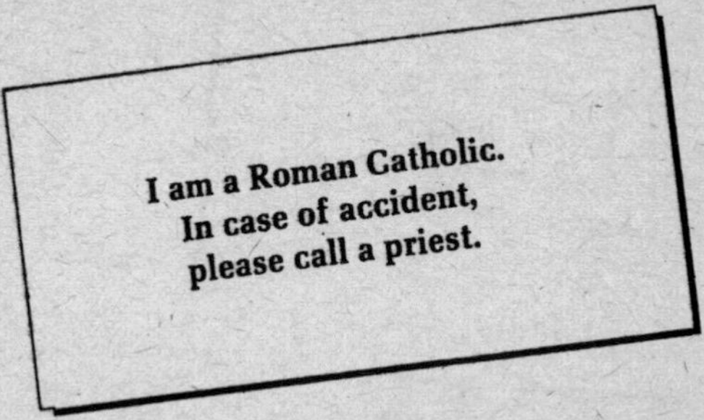

I am a Roman Catholic.
In case of accident,
please call a priest.

one shown here. These cards bear vital information, which can be of great help to the people who come across the body. And now—with this necessary, but thoroughly dull, introduction out of the way, let us herewith present a random selection of

IN-CASE-OF-EMERGENCY CARDS for Special People

WRITER: FRANK JACOBS

I am a physical coward.
In case of accident,
please tell me my
wounds are superficial.

I am a neurotic beset by traumas
dating back to my childhood.
In case of death, call up
my father and tell him
I forgive him.

I am a Christian Scientist.
In case of illness,
it's just your imagination.

I am Harold Pemberton, who,
until a recent operation, used
to be known as Harriet Pemberton.
In case of serious injury,
tell the doctor not to be too
surprised at what he finds.

I am a masochist.
In case of accident, please
don't call anyone. Just let me
lie back and enjoy it.

I am a Jewish Mother.
In case of stroke, nervous
collapse or, God forbid, pains
in my chest, call my son
and tell him it is
much worse than it looks.

I am the leader of a spiritualist cult. In case of death, notify my followers to expect me at their next seance.

I am a Mafia Don. In case of sudden accident, call my Capo and tell him to rub out "Legs" Fazio.

I am a Garment Center Executive. In case of mortal accident, phone my partner, Sol, and tell him I'll be watching him from Up There.

I am a lawyer.
Should I be hospitalized and
fail to pull through,
institute a suit for malpractice.

I AM A VAMPIRE
In case of accident, my
blood types are A, O, AB, X,
RH Negative & RH Positive.

I am Billy Smithers,
age 5. In case of
accident, please
give the Frog in my
pocket a good home

Hi! I'm **Mark Spritz!** I'm famous for being a **Gold Medal Winner!** Unfortunately, I'm also a **Silver coin LOSER!** Mainly, I lost a **toss** with **MAD's Editor** ... and now I'm stuck doing one of these idiotic interviews. So here I am with my special guest, **Mr. Randolph Ripoff,** who's been chosen

MAD'S "SINGLES ONLY" RESORT OWNER OF THE YEAR

ARTIST: GEORGE WOODBRIDGE   WRITER: LOU SILVERSTONE

...And are today's Singles any different from the guests you USED to have here?

Of course! These kids are WITH IT! They're LIBERATED! All we got in the old days were ugly fat Secretaries ...and homely dull Accountants!

So, at great personal sacrifice, I converted to "Singles Only"!

I hired a Sign Painter to change the name! Sign Painters don't come cheap these days!

What great personal sacrifice?

Uh ... all I can see are ugly fat Secretaries and homely dull Accountants NOW!

May be true! But they're all "Swinging Single" Secretaries and Accountants! What did you expect at a place like this—Joe Namath and Gloria Steinem?

They may look like the same losers, but there's a big difference! See—Madison Avenue discovered the buying power of the Singles, and gave them a new, cool, swinging IMAGE! Just look at the casual way they dress!

It's casual, all right ... but how come they're all dressed ALIKE??

Well, part of the Swinger's creed is to do whatever is IN! Or, to put it another way, if you want to be a Non-Conformist, you have to CONFORM! And these—er—Non-Conformist Uniforms can only be purchased here ... exclusively at Ripoff's!

RIPOFF'S BOUTIQUE

WEAR YOUR OWN THING

SPECIAL NONCONFORMIST CLOTHES FOR THE CHUBBY, HUSKY, HARD-TO-FIT

Do you have planned activities or do your guests find ways to amuse themselves?

If we didn't tell these Pepsi Generation Swingers what to do 24 hours a day, they'd do nothing but eat! I figure it's cheaper to amuse them than feed them! So we offer real far-out activities like ping-pong, volley ball, hula hoops, yo-yo's, beer busts, bridge tournaments, Simon says, handball, tennis, shuffleboard, bocce and Mambo Lessons!

They don't sound very far out! Most of the other Singles Clubs I know have wild things like Sky Diving and Mountain Climbing!

If any of these overweight slobs climbed an ANTHILL, they'd collapse! But we do have a hot air balloon! It's the best investment I ever made! Hop aboard!

YOUNG DOCTOF

FREEN

If you live in a big city . . . or a small town, for that matter . . . the odds are that sooner or later you're gonna be mugged! So, as a public service, MAD offers these lines of dialogue calculated to

BLUFF THAT MUGGER!

ARTIST: BRUCE DAY   WRITER: E. NELSON BRIDWELL

Gee, you're the **first** person that's **spoken** to me since I escaped from the Insane Asylum's **Violent Ward!**

Help yourself! I just want to **warn** you! Since I saw **"Papillon,"** I keep my money in a **strange place!**

Beat it! There's a **Mafia Contract** out on me, and anybody that's **seen** with me is as good as **dead!**

You're **welcome to it!** I'm sick and tired of trying to **pass** these marked bills from the **ransom!**

Congratulations! You're gonna be the **tenth mugger** I've killed this month with my **Kung Fu!**

Sure, I've got something for you! Where do you want it . . . in the **belly** or the **head?**

Great! This'll give me a good **workout** for my upcoming **title fight** with **Foreman!**

No, no! You're doing it all **wrong!** Let an **EXPERIENCED** mugger show you **how!**

I like your **style,** kid! How'd you like to move up to where the **REAL dough** is?

Next time anybody bombards you with an irritating old cliché, don't just stand there! Say something! Something . . . NASTY!! Yes, squelch any mindless babbler who tries to drop a cliché on you by zapping him with an appropriate answer chosen from

MAD'S

SURE-FIRE

CLICHÉ

KILLERS

ARTIST: JACK DAVIS   WRITER: STAN HART

CLICHES

On paper, the Kings are a great team!

Yeah, but on ice, they stink!

Pound for pound . . . he's the greatest!

I don't know! Pound for pound, I like steak better!

That kid plays on sheer guts!

Too bad he can't hit or field!

Well . . . there's no tomorrow!

I wish I could have said that yesterday!

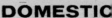

CLICHES

I don't play favorites! I love you **both** the same!

Gee, Sis! I didn't know **YOU** had a **lousy** deal, **TOO!**

Must you **gulp** your food?

I want to get it **down** before the taste catches up with me!

Don't raise your voice to me! What will the neighbor's think?

They'll think **DAD's** home!

I have to bend down and **pick** up **after you** all day long!

Well, it's **cheaper** than going to **Jack LaLanne!**

CLICHES

CLICHES

How about a **delicious** breakfast?

No, I think I'll eat this instead!

Take **two** aspirin and call me in the **morning!**

If two aspirin would do any **good**, I **wouldn't** be calling you **now!**

I think you'll live! *Ha-ha!*

Great! That means you're sending me to **another Doctor!**

Don't worry! I've performed **dozens** of these operations!

Any **successfully??**

CLICHES

ONE
SATURDAY MORNING
IN A
SUPERMARKET

CHAKUNK-DING-RIP

PICTURE ROAD SIGNS

FOR EVERYDAY SITUATIONS

ARTIST: JACK RICKARD

WRITER: PAUL PETER PORGES

"IMMEDIATE SERVICE . . . OR NO TIP!!"

"GET A HAIRCUT!"

"NO RAISE!"

"NOT TONIGHT! I'VE GOT A HEADACHE!"

"DON'T TRY ANYTHING! I'M A KARATE EXPERT!"

"NO COMMENT!"

"YOUR CIGAR STINKS!"

"DON'T BUG ME!"

"ASK YOUR MOTHER!"

Hi! I'm **Mason Reach,** this issue's **"Sports Personality Interviewer!"** Why **Me** . . . and not somebody more suitable, like **Howard Cosell? Because!** So **there!** Now, let's get on with it, and meet **Royal "Bear" Hades,** who's been chosen as . . .

MAD'S
COLLEGE FOOTBALL

COACH OF THE YEAR

Yeah . . . Hey, all you kids out there! Run down to the store now, and buy my book, "Losing Is Un-American!" It'll not only teach you how to be a winner in the game of **FOOTBALL,** but in the game of **LIFE!**

Does your book teach **clean play, honesty** and **sportsmanship?**

Of course not! My book teaches you how to **WIN!** Listen, kid, **NOBODY** wins using those stupid tactics!

How do you think **your** team would do against a **PRO TEAM?**

Sonny! My team **IS** a Pro Team! Our payroll is **higher** than half the teams in the **NFL!**

ARTIST: JACK DAVIS   WRITER: LOU SILVERSTONE

Coach Hades, what's the **most important ingredient** in being a successful coach?

A **College President** who wants a **winning team**, and doesn't care **how** he gets it!

C'mon . . . I'll show you around! This is one of our **Dressing Rooms** . . .

This—this **CLOSET** is where your team dresses for a game?!?

Nah! This is where the **VISITING team** dresses for a game! Today, games are won on **two** fields: the field of **play**, and the field of **psychology**! You'd be surprised how a crummy dressing room like this can **demoralize** an opposing team!

And this is my star substitute!

He's not much bigger than me! What position does he play?

He doesn't play! He substitutes for my first team players when they have to take exams! He may only weigh 130, but his I.Q. is 160!

C'mon! Let's see some HITTING out there! HIT! HIT! STICK . . .

If that's the team, they don't look much like Football Players!

They're not! They sell programs, hot dogs and the rest of the goodies! My contract calls for 10% of the concessions! C'mon, you slobs! Lets see some hustle! There's gonna be 60,000 people out there Saturday! Move!

Hey, look— we gotta practice Friday night when "Sanford and Son" is on the TV!!

What's wrong with our Publicity Department?! I haven't been on one magazine cover all season! How'm I gonna win the Heisman Trophy with no cover stories?

Do all of your players gripe like that', Coach Hades?

They wouldn't **dare**! Anybody that don't like the way I **run** things can turn in his uniform! Having **malcontents** around is bad for **team moral**!

Then **how** come you don't throw **THOSE two** off the team?

Because **THAT** would be bad for **MY** moral! They're both **All-American**!

Do you have any **special plays** you use against particularly tough teams?

Here's one I dreamed up . . . "**The Hidden Key**" play . . .

When the opposing team gets to their **dressing room** at half-time, they find the **door locked**! By the time the **Field Superintendent** is located, and comes up with the **Master Key**, the other team has spent ten or fifteen minutes standing around in a **drafty corridor**, getting **no rest** . . . with no time to plan **second half strategy**!

Gee . . . isn't he kinda **YOUNG** to be recruited, Coach Hades?!?

Take it easy, girls! This **isn't** a recruit! This is **Mason Reach**, from **MAD!** I was telling him how you girls keep our visiting High School stars from getting **homesick** while they're here, looking over our Campus!

Hey! How old **ARE** you, anyway, kid?

Gee! How does **that** help recruit 'em?

Coaches are famous for their **inspirational speeches!** Can you recall your **best one?**

Sure, "If you want a station wagon that's **tough, economical** and **roomy,** try the triple —threat Shlock 360!"

I meant to the **players!** You know, a speech that **fires them** up to play their **best ball . . .**

I don't **bother** with those silly things anymore! I inspire our guys with **cash bonuses** for **good games** and a giant **jackpot** for whoever wipes out the other team's **quarterback!**

Here's the place! As soon as I finish studying this "Scouting Report," we'll go in!

Does that report tell you all about the player?

I know all about him! This is a report on his parents!

You mean you scout the parents?

Of course! The key to successful recruiting is to know the correct way to approach the parents . . . which ones should be bribed, which ones should be buttered up, which ones should be conned, and so forth!

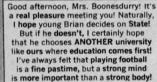

Good afternoon, Mrs. Boonesdurry! It's a real pleasure meeting you! Naturally, I hope young Brian decides on State! But if he doesn't, I certainly hope that he chooses ANOTHER university like ours where education comes first! I've always felt that playing football is a fine pastime, but a strong mind is more important than a strong body!

It certainly is refreshing talking to you, Mr. Hades! Those other coaches that were here offered Brian all kinds of money and cars . . . it was so disgusting!!

Ahhh! Those creeps don't bother me! I just signed a ten-year, no-cut, iron-clad contract to coach here at State! I want to spend the rest of my career at this great school! And if I ever get married and have sons, I want them to come to State! I've recruited every boy on this team personally, and they're loyal to me! And that's what I like in a boy . . . LOYALTY!!

BEAT MIDWESTERN!

RRING!

Pardon me, son! I gotta take this call!

Yes? Speaking! How much? Listen, I get that already! Up it another ten grand a year, throw in "Athletic Director" and you got a deal! Fine! I'll settle up my business here, and I'll be there faster than you can say "Beat State"!

Listen, kid! I got a scoop for you! You are now looking at the new "Coach and Athletic Director" of Midwestern U.!

But—but what about "loyalty," and your ten-year iron-clad contract with State?

RIP!

BEAT MIDWESTERN!

Contracts were **made to be broken**, kid! Football is a **tough racket**, and a man has to look out for **himself!** Also, I owe it to my **family** to take this great **opportunity!**

WHAT family . . .?!?

My **two dogs** and my **parakeet!** Besides, it's a **challenge!!** The stadium **there** holds **80,000 . . .!**

But what about all the **players** you recruited, and all the **promises** you made to their **parents . . .?**

That's **THEIR** problem! Of course, any players that **haven't** enrolled yet, I can take **with** me! After all, Midwestern U. is a **fine school** with a great **tradition**, and if I ever have **sons**, I'd want **them** to go to Midwestern . . .

I think this is where we **came in**, so . . . this is **Mason Reach**, signing off for **MAD Magazine!**

IT ALMOST RESTORES YOUR FAITH WHEN...

ARTIST: JACK RICKARD
WRITER: LOU SILVERSTONE

IT ALMOST RESTORES YOUR FAITH WHEN . . .

. . . a Hippie hits you up for bus fare

. . . and you actually see him on the bus!

. . . you neglect to study for an exam

. . . and the teacher fails to show up!

IT ALMOST RESTORES YOUR FAITH WHEN ...

Narcs hit your dorm in a surprise bust

... and all they find is cigarettes!

IT ALMOST RESTORES YOUR FAITH WHEN . . .

. . . you're called down to the Internal Revenue Service for an income tax audit

. . . and they discover that you've got a refund coming!

IT ALMOST RESTORES YOUR FAITH WHEN . . .

. . . your car breaks down, and you're
stranded in the middle of nowhere

. . . and there's a pay phone nearby
that's actually in good working order!

IT ALMOST RESTORES YOUR FAITH WHEN . . .

. . . some pickpocket
rips off your wallet

. . . and then mails it back to you with the
money gone, but your vital papers intact!

IT ALMOST RESTORES YOUR FAITH WHEN . . .

You go on a date with the biggest make-out girl on Campus, and you don't even score

. . . and then you find out she gave a social disease to six guys who DID!

IT ALMOST RESTORES YOUR FAITH WHEN . . .

. . . you're involved in a terrible
auto accident with a drunken driver

. . . and the only person who's
injured is the drunken driver!

IT ALMOST RESTORES YOUR FAITH WHEN . . .

. . . the candidate you worked so hard
for is badly beaten in the election

. . . and then it's discovered that the man who
beat him is involved in an election scandal!

Today, a silent war is raging (And sometimes, it's not so silent!) between "Smokers" and "Non-Smokers." Smokers are strong-willed and determined, insisting upon their God-given right to kill themselves. And Non-Smokers are equally strong-willed and determined, insisting upon their God-given right to breathe fresh air instead of that murderous Smokers' smoke. All kinds of solutions have been tried, such as "No-Smoking" sections in theaters, trains and planes, but with little success. (Like, how are you going to keep the smoke in the "Smoking Section" from wafting over to the "No Smoking" section?) And there are countless other places where Non-Smokers don't even have this minimal protection, such as offices, restaurants and even private homes. However, MAD feels that, with a little cooperation from both our Smokers and our Non-Smokers, the war between them can be happily ended . . . mainly by the use of these

MAD DEVICES

DESIGNED TO SOLVE OUR SMOKER VS. NON-SMOKER PROBLEMS

ARTIST & WRITER: AL JAFFEE

THE PROBLEM

A SHORT ACCOUNT OF A NON-SMOKER'S DILEMMA

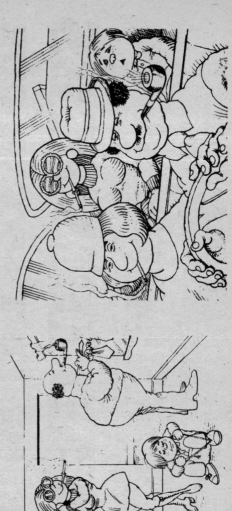

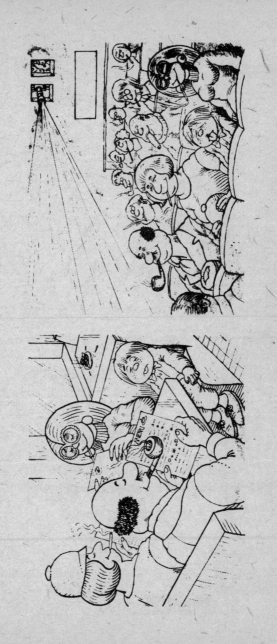

MAD'S PUBLIC AND PRIVATE GROUP SMOKE FILTERING AND EXHAUST SYSTEM DEVICES

DECORATIVE SMOKE-EXHAUSTING DINING TABLE VASE

Individual, sterilized mouthpieces and tubes are supplied by host. Each one is plugged into the vase, where a powerful exhaust system removes the smoke to the utter delight of non-smokers at the table.

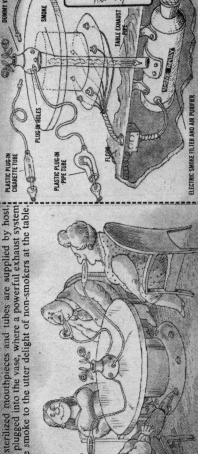

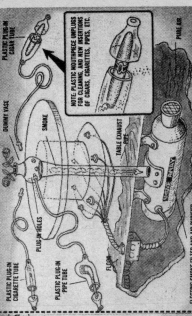

PLASTIC PLUG-IN CIGAR TUBE

DUMMY VASE

NOTE: PLASTIC MOUTHPIECE UNPLUGS FOR CLEANING, AND NEW INSERTIONS OF CIGARS, CIGARETTES, PIPES, ETC.

SMOKE

PLASTIC PLUG-IN CIGARETTE TUBE

PLASTIC PLUG-IN PIPE TUBE

PLUG-IN HOLES

TABLE EXHAUST PIPE

FLOOR

PURE AIR

ELECTRIC SMOKE FILTER AND AIR PURIFIER

THE RESTAURANT SMOKER'S PERSONAL EXHAUST SYSTEM

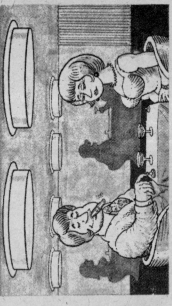

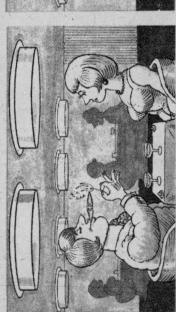

After a hearty meal, the restaurant diner lights up, much to the dismay of his date, who is a non-smoker, and pales with the anticipation of inhaling nauseating cigar smoke.

But unknown to her, restaurant has considerately installed a Smoker's Personal Exhaust System, which the smoker puts into operation by pressing button at his corner of table.

Button activates individual Smoker's Personal Exhaust System, which lowers large plexiglass tube over diner.

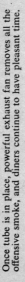

Once tube is in place, powerful exhaust fan removes all the offensive smoke, and diners continue to have pleasant time.

THEATER, PLANE, TRAIN, BUS, ETC. EXHAUST MASKS

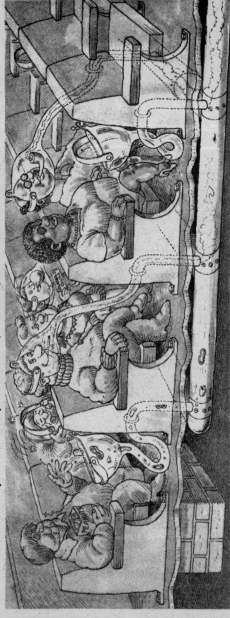

Any situation with crowded, fixed seats can be adapted to this 100% effective Smoke Control System. It eliminates impractical "Smoking" and "No Smoking" sections, and the splitting up of smoker–non-smoker friends and relatives.

COMPLETELY SELF-CONTAINED ASHTRAY FILTER SYSTEM

This compact and effective device runs on batteries or house current, and will draw smoke from as far as twenty feet away. Can also be used as ordinary air-cleaner for pollen, dust, etc.

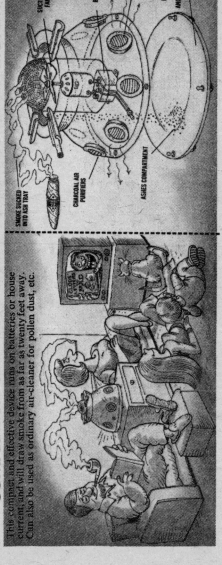

SUCTION FAN

BATTERY

PURIFIED AIR EXHAUSTED HERE

REMOVABLE BOTTOM FOR CLEANING AND BATTERY REPLACEMENT

SMOKE SUCKED INTO ASH TRAY

CHARCOAL AIR PURIFIERS

ASHES COMPARTMENT

UTILITARIAN SMOKE-EXHAUSTING CHANDELIER SYSTEM

This attractive and unobtrusive device serves the double purpose of light fixture and smoke remover.

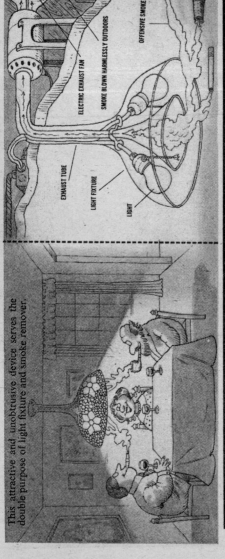

ELECTRIC EXHAUST FAN

SMOKE BLOWN HARMLESSLY OUTDOORS

OFFENSIVE SMOKE

EXHAUST TUBE

LIGHT FIXTURE

LIGHT

MAD'S SMOKE-FILLED, CROWDED ROOM DEVICES

The smoke-filled, crowded room presents a special problem that the ordinary, simple filtering device cannot handle conveniently or dependably. Here, then, are two sure-fire solutions that can take the smoke headache out of hosting.

THE GIGANTIC CEILING GRID & ATTIC BLOWER EXHAUST SYSTEM

THE GIGANTIC FLOOR GRID AND CELLAR BLOWER EXHAUST SYSTE

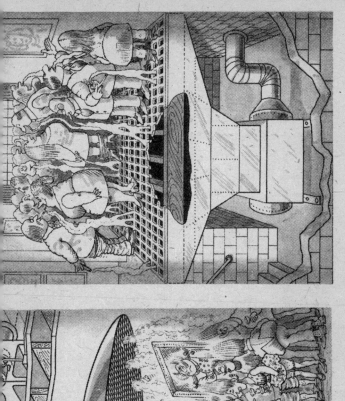

PERSONAL DEVICES FOR INDIVIDUAL SMOKERS

SMOKER'S AIR PURIFYING AND SMOKE FILTERING HAT

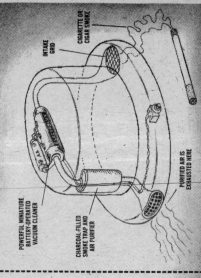

CIGARETTE OR CIGAR SMOKE

INTAKE GRID

POWERFUL MINIATURE BATTERY-OPERATED VACUUM CLEANER

CHARCOAL-FILLED SMOKE TRAP AND AIR PURIFIER

PURIFIED AIR IS EXHAUSTED HERE

Upon meeting non-smoking friend, the smoker considerately presses a button on what appears to be a plain straw (or other style) hat.

Suddenly, all smoke emanating from the smoker's cigarette or cigar miraculously disappears almost as fast as it is made.

SMOKER'S PERSONAL MASK & CANE FILTERING DEVICE

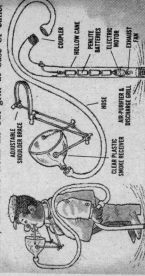

Clear mask is supported by adjustable shoulder brace. Powerful mini-motor pulls smoke into mask, through a filter, and sends clean air out grill at base of cane.

COUPLER
HOLLOW CANE
PENLITE BATTERIES
ELECTRIC MOTOR
EXHAUST FAN
ADJUSTABLE SHOULDER BRACE
HOSE
CLEAR PLASTIC SMOKE RECEIVER
AIR-PURIFIER & DISCHARGE GRILL

This principle can also be adapted for use with umbrellas, swagger sticks, crutches, stilts and other walking devices.

SMOKER'S DUMMY EYEGLASS SMOKE EXHAUSTING DEVICE

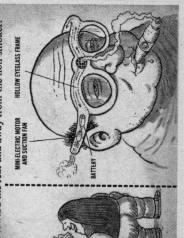

Smoke is drawn directly into grill located on eyeglass nose bridge piece, and then blown inoffensively through earpieces toward the rear and away from the non-smoker.

HOLLOW EYEGLASS FRAME
MINI-ELECTRIC MOTOR AND SUCTION FAN
BATTERY

SMOKER'S SHOPPING CART SMOKE FILTERING SYSTEM

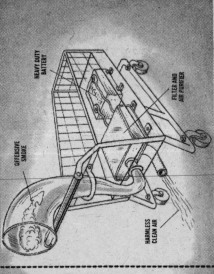

Shoppers can blithely and happily push these carts around without fear of stinking up entire store. Also reduces fire hazard so that many stores which do not permit smoking can now offer it as bonus.

SELF-PROTECTIVE DEVICES FOR NON-SMOKERS

NON-SMOKER'S LAPEL FLOWER REAR SMOKE DISSIPATOR

Powerful mini-blower pulls smelly smoke into dummy flower and sends it harmlessly out rear. Also effective against bad breath.

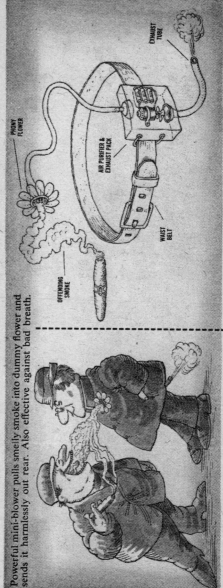

EXHAUST TUBE

PHONY FLOWER

AIR PURIFIER & EXHAUST PACK

WAIST BELT

OFFENDING SMOKE

NON-SMOKER'S REAR INTAKE
EYEGLASS AIR PURIFIER

Smoke being blown into non-smoker's face does not bother him because he breathes pure air taken from behind him.

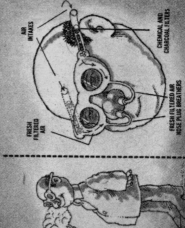

AIR INTAKES

CHEMICAL AND CHARCOAL FILTERS

FRESH FILTERED AIR

FRESH FILTERED AIR NOSE PLUG BREATHERS

NON-SMOKER'S FOUNTAIN
PEN SMOKE SUCTION FILTER

A marvel of miniaturization, this pen is a complete smoke filtering and air purifying plant and is carried easily.

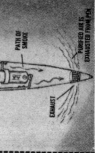

OFFENSIVE SMOKE IS SUCKED INTO PEN

MINI-MOTOR AND AIR PURIFIER

BATTERY

PATH OF SMOKE

SMOKE

INDUCTION GRID

PHONY PEN CASE

EXHAUST

PURIFIED AIR IS EXHAUSTED FROM PEN

NON-SMOKER'S DECORATIVE BROOCH SMOKE EXHAUSTER

Attractive and easy to wear, smoke is drawn into brooch and pumped through hose to grill at wearer's back. This takes smoke (and breath) away from non-smoker's face.

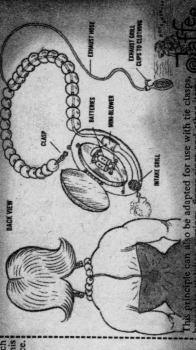

BACK VIEW

CLASP

BATTERIES

MINI-BLOWER

INTAKE GRILL

EXHAUST HOSE

EXHAUST GRILL
CLIPS TO CLOTHING

This principle can also be adapted for use with tie clasps, bracelets, watches, earrings, finger rings and other items.

ONE BEAUTIFUL EVENING LAST MAY

THE LIGHTER SIDE OF...

ANXIETY

ARTIST & WRITER:
DAVE BERG

No more **insecurity**! No more **anxiety**! I've **played** that game for the **last time**! I'm **bowing out** of the rat race!

My wife and I have **wiped the slate clean**! We're starting out on a **new Life Style** . . . with **new priorities**! We're looking to a future based on **solid standards**, with **deep permanent roots** and **long meaningful relationships**!

Sounds great! How are you going to **do** that?

We sold our home, and got ourselves a **trailer**!

SOLD

I **can't stand** these new super highways! Everybody on 'em drives like a **maniac!**

It's like every driver is hell-bent on speeding to an **accident!** . . . his **OWN!!**

You're a **fine** one to talk! You're driving **faster** than anyone else around!

That's because I want to **get OFF** this blasted highway as **soon** as I **can!**

What a weekend! Have I got **trouble**! Friday, my super-bright **kid** announces he's dropping out of college!

You call that **trouble**?

With **money** so tight, my wife picks Friday to suddenly go out on a **wild spending spree**!

You call that trouble?

Business is so **lousy** that on Friday, my **Accountant** tells me I won't be able to make **next week's** payroll!

You call that trouble?

Friday night, my **television** set blew . . . and I had to go through the **whole weekend WITHOUT IT!!**

Now, **THAT'S TROUBLE!!**

That's not a civilized city out there! It's a JUNGLE!

In the old days, they only used to rip off blind newsdealers and little old ladies! But now, they're so desperate that even big, strong, heathy-looking guys like us can be victimized!

I—I never thought I'd be afraid to go out there and make a few bucks!

We're just gonna have to find some other way to make our bread . . .

. . . besides mugging!!

Changes . . . changes! They're coming so **rapidly** that it's making me into a **neurotic**!

My big virile **Son** has turned into a **style freak,** and now he dresses like a **pansy**! My little feminine **Daughter** has become a **Women's Libber,** and now she dresses like a **farmer**!

I'd go **completely** out of my mind if it wasn't for **your wonderful reliable stability**!

You dressed like a slob in the past . . . and you're **STILL** a slob!!

Oooh, I've got a terrible pain in my **chest!** I think I'm **dying!**

Again?! You're the world's greatest hypochondriac!

You keep going to **Doctors,** and they all keep telling you the same thing . . . that it's **just EMOTIONAL!** And then, the pain moves to **another** spot!

Do you **understand?!?** It's **PSYCHOSOMATIC!** It's **IN YOUR MIND!!**

Y'know, you're **right!**

Now . . . I've got a terrible **headache!** I think I'm **dying!**

David Berg

A MAD LOOK AT

SUPER HEROES

ARTIST & WRITER: SERGIO ARAGONES

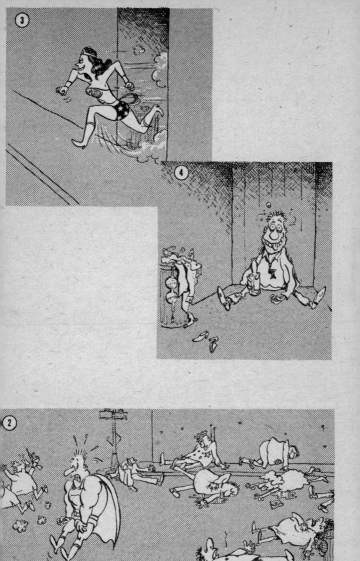

One of the silliest trends on TV the past few seasons has been "The Ethnic Detective Show." We've had Banaceck, Kodiak, Kolchak, Nakia . . . and one guy who's become the top-rated TV Cop of them all. Yes,

Where's Kojerk!?

Kojerk? I think he's at the Barber Shop . . . having his "skin" styled!

No, I think he took the squad car to Fanny Farmer to stock up on lollipops!

No, he's buying another of those $350 suits he can amazingly afford on a Cop's salary!

we're talking about that charismic, burly Greek with the cute mannerisms and the gleaming skull. So, lower the "brightness" in your room, and get ready for MAD's version of . . .

JERK

ARTIST: ANGELO TORRES

WRITER: ARNIE KOGEN

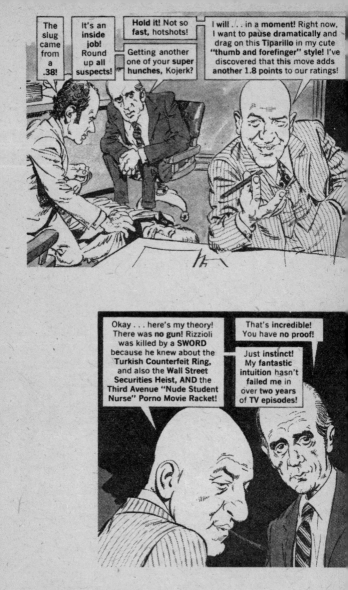

Okay, this is our first stop!

Hey, you . . . send out twelve of your best-lookin' broads!

A Call-Girl Operation?!? You think Rizzioli's killer is a hooker?!?

Nahhh! Now that I'm a SUPER STAR, I want to re-do "The Dirty Dozen" MY way!!

You punk! You creep! I oughtta kill you!

Take it easy, Kojerk! This guy don't look like no MURDERER!!

I know! I just like to punch around anyone on this show who dresses better than me!

I think our killer may be in there! It's a big "Hood Hangout!" Wait for me! I'm going in alone . . . but in a clever disguise!

Listen, don't go in there, Kojerk! It could be very dangerous!

PARK

Kojerk . . . how come you're always dating **Police Women . . . ?**

I like taking the **Law** into my own hands!

Well, I'm off to the **Statue of Liberty!** I'm gonna **slap her around** a little! I think the Lady of Steel **knows** a lot **more** than she's **telling**, an I'm gonna—

I'm afraid it's **too late** for your crazy hunches, Kojerk! We've **found** our murderer!

You—you **have?** Who **is** it . . . ?

STAYFROZE! Those **plants** he's been growing for two years were **Marijuana!** Rizzioli **found out** about it, and Stayfroze **killed** him! So it turns out **Stayfroze** is the "**heavy**" in this story!

He's **not** the **heavy!** He's my **Brother!**